This book belongs to

....

make
believe
ideas

Rumpelstiltskin

Key sound ar spellings:
a, ar, are, au, ear
Secondary sounds: sk, sp, st

Written by Rosie Greening
Illustrated by Clare Fennell

Reading with phonics

How to use this book

The **Reading with phonics** series helps you to have fun with your child and to support their learning of phonics and reading. It is aimed at children who have learned the letter sounds and are building confidence in their reading.

Each title in the series focuses on a different key sound or blend of sounds. The entertaining retelling of the story repeats this sound frequently, and the different spellings for the sound or blend of sounds are highlighted in red type. The first activity at the back of the book provides practice in reading and using words containing this sound or blend of sounds. The key sound for **Rumpelstiltskin** is **ar**.

Start by reading the story to your child, asking them to join in with the refrain in bold. Next, encourage them to read the story with you. Give them a hand to decode tricky words.

Now look at the activity pages at the back of the book. These are intended for you and your child to enjoy together. Most are not activities to complete in pencil or pen, but by reading and talking or pointing.

The **Key sound** pages focus on one sound, and on the various different groups of letters that produce that sound. Encourage your child to read the different letter groups and complete the activity, so they become more aware of the variety of spellings there are for the same sound.

The **Letters together** pages look at three pairs or groups of letters and at the sounds they make as they work together. Help your child to read the words and trace the routes on the word maps.

Rhyme is used a lot in these retellings. Whatever stage your child has reached in their learning of phonics, it is always good practice for them to listen carefully for sounds and find words that rhyme. The pages on **Rhyming words** take six words from the story and ask children to read and find other words that rhyme with them.

The **Key words** pages focus on a number of key words that occur regularly but can nonetheless be challenging. Many of these words are not sounded out following the rules of phonics and the easiest thing is for children to learn them by sight, so that they do not worry about decoding them. These pages encourage children to retell the story, practising key words as they do so.

The **Picture dictionary** page asks children to focus closely on nine words from the story. Encourage children to look carefully at each word, cover it with their hand, write it on a separate piece of paper, and finally, check it!

Do not complete all the activities at once – doing one each time you read will ensure that your child continues to enjoy the stories and the time you are spending together. **Have fun!**

There was a castle, large and old,
with walls made out of sparkling gold.
Inside lived Mark, the charming King,
who loved gold more than anything.

Old Farmer Clark was marching by
and told King Mark a harmful lie:
"My daughter, Kate, is smart," he said.
"She spins straw into golden thread!"

A farmer tells a lie today,
near King Mark's castle, far away.

"This girl's my perfect match!" Mark said,
and locked Kate in a straw-filled shed.
He left a harsh and harmful note:
"Turn all the straw to gold," he wrote.

Kate tried to start, but thought, "I'm through!
This job is far too hard to do."
She lay down in the straw to weep,
but just as she dropped off to sleep . . .

Kate's in the dark, but has to stay
in King Mark's castle, far away.

The girl heard something in the dark.
A POP, then lots of scarlet sparks!
A tiny dancing man appeared,
who wore a scarf and had a beard!

"My dear, your problems are quite large.
I'll help you if you pay my charge.
Give me that garnet charm you hold,
and I'll spin piles of sparkling gold."

POP!

A garnet charm Kate has to pay,
in King Mark's castle, far away.

By dawn, the straw was golden thread.
When Mark marched in, he lost his head.
"You star!" he laughed, and with a grin,
he found more straw for Kate to spin.

10

Poor Kate declared, "I'm smart, it's true.
But this is far too hard to do!"
Then with some sparks of scarlet light,
the dancing man was back in sight.

The task is hard, to Kate's dismay,
in King Mark's castle, far away.

Kate saw the man and gave a yelp.
"King Mark has lost his marbles – help!"
The man said, "I don't spin for free:
will you give your first child to me?"

Kate nodded with a sinking heart,
and watched the man sit down and start.
By morning, all the straw had gone,
and in its place, gold thread now shone.

He laughs and spins without delay,
in King Mark's castle, far away.

13

When Mark charged in, he said, "You are
the smartest girl I've met, by far!"
The charming King bent on one knee
and said, "Please will you marry me?"

The pair were married on that day.
(Kate smartly threw the wheel away.)
And soon, they had a *baby boy*
who filled their hearts with love and joy.

The king and Kate were wed that day,
in King Mark's castle, far away.

A few months later, in the dark,
Kate spotted lots of scarlet sparks.
The little man jumped out and smiled.
He said, "It's time. Give me your child!"

This wasn't what Kate bargained for.
"Take something else – I've gold galore!"
Said he, "I'd rather play a game.
To keep your child, just guess my name!"

It breaks her heart, Kate has to play,
in King Mark's castle, far away.

For days, Kate searched around for clues.
She wept and said, "I'm going to lose!"
At last, a farmer came to speak.
She said, "I know the name you seek!"

"In a market square, I overheard
an artful man sing out these words:
'The queen will never win my game,
for Rumpelstiltskin is my name!'"

The farmer knows what Kate should say,
in King Mark's castle, far away.

The man appeared and barked, "It's time!
If you guess wrong, your child is mine!"

Kate said, "It's not too hard to do.
RUMPELSTILTSKIN – yes, that's you!"

Kate does her part and saves the day,
near King Mark's castle, far away.

The man was startled as can be!
His scarlet face scowled angrily.

POP!

Then with a POP, Rumpel was gone –
and Kate was free from that day on!

The smart queen was set free that day,
in King Mark's castle, far away.

Key sound

There are several different groups of letters that make the **ar** sound. Practise them by following Rumpelstiltskin's golden threads to the treasure. Can you use each word in a different sentence?

castle

hearth

aunt

large

Mark

nasty

heart

rather

barn

laugh

dark

smart

hard

star

25

Letters together

Look at these pairs of letters and
say the sounds they make.

st   sk   sp

Follow the words that contain **st** to
help King Mark find his castle.

st

smart

start

fast

straw

queen

farmer

castle

Follow the words that contain **sk** to help Kate do her tasks.

sk — ask — mask
whisk — desk
man — risk
guess — tasks — thread

Follow the words that contain **sp** to help Kate spin some gold.

sp — gold
king
speak — spark — spot
house — scarlet — spin

Rhyming words

Read and say the words in the flowers and point to other words that rhyme with them.

start	**smart**	child
heart		large

ask	**task**	gold
castle		mask

grin	**spin**	man
tin		star

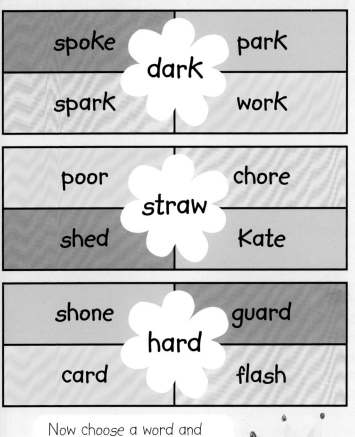

spoke	park
dark	
spark	work

poor	chore
straw	
shed	Kate

shone	guard
hard	
card	flash

Now choose a word and make up a rhyming chant!

Kate sees **sparks** in the **dark park**!

Key words

Many common words can be tricky to sound out. Practise them by reading these sentences about the story. Now make more sentences using other key words from around the border.

King Mark lived **in** a gold castle.

Farmer Clark told King Mark **a** lie.

Mark locked Kate in a shed full **of** straw.

Kate was sad because **she** couldn't spin gold.

called · their · asked · got · it

· children · off · a · he · very · made · are · put · we ·

She **asked** Rumpelstiltskin for help.

He turned all the straw into gold.

Mark was happy **when** he saw the gold.

Kate **had** to guess Rumpelstiltskin's name.

A farmer told Kate what he was **called**.

Rumpelstiltskin vanished **with** a pop.

all · saw · and · in · them · let · wanted · mum · she · when · up · you · had ·

old · there · were · into · of · with · make · some ·

Picture dictionary

Look carefully at the pictures and the words.
Now cover the words, one at a time.
Can you remember how to write them?

castle

charm

child

farmer

king

man

spinning
wheel

straw

thread